MINIONS
BANANA!

Art by: **RENAUD COLLIN**   Written by: **DIDIER AH-KOON**

ISBN 9781782765592
Published by Titan Comics, a division of Titan Publishing Group Ltd.
144 Southwark St. London, SE1 0UP.

10 9 8 7 6 5 4 3 2 1
A CIP catalogue record for this title is available from the British Library.
Titan Comics. TCN 0867

Printed in Italy

Editorial
Senior Editor Natalie Clubb Designer Russell Seal
Titan Comics
Studio Manager Selina Juneja
Production Supervisors Peter James, Jackie Flook, Maria Pearson
Production Manager Obi Onuora
Senior Sales Manager Steve Tothill
Commercial Manager Michelle Fairlamb
Direct Sales & Marketing Manager Ricky Claydon
Publishing Manager Darryl Tothill
Publishing Director Chris Teather
Operations Director Leigh Baulch
Executive Director Vivian Cheung
Publisher Nick Landau

Titan
COMICS

030

RENAUD + DiDiER 2014

Renaud + Didier 2014

STRETCHING

09

RENAUD + DIDIER 2014

RENAUD + DIDIER 2014

REVAUD + DIDIER 2014

RENAUD + DIDIER 2014

REVAUD + DIDIER 2014

03

RENAUD + DIDIER 2014

RENAUD + DIDIER 2014

RENAUD + DIDIER 2014

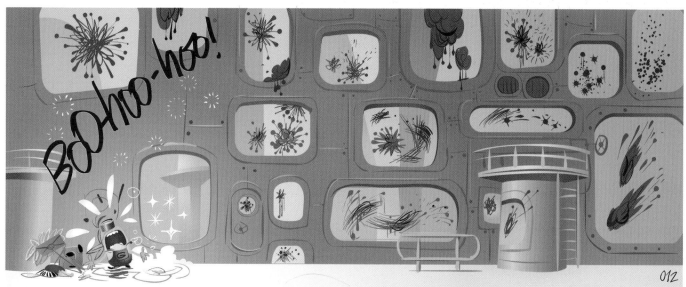

Renaud + Didier 2014

REVAUD + DIDIER 2014

Renaud + Didier 2014

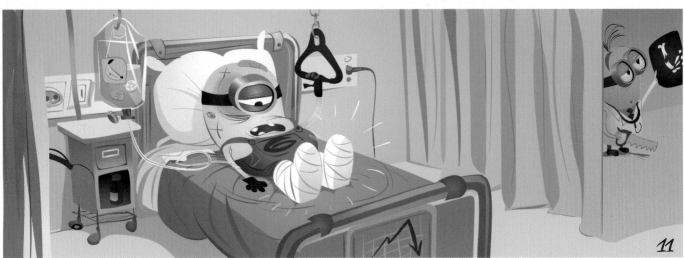

RENAUD + DIDIER 2014

RENAUD + DIDIER 2014

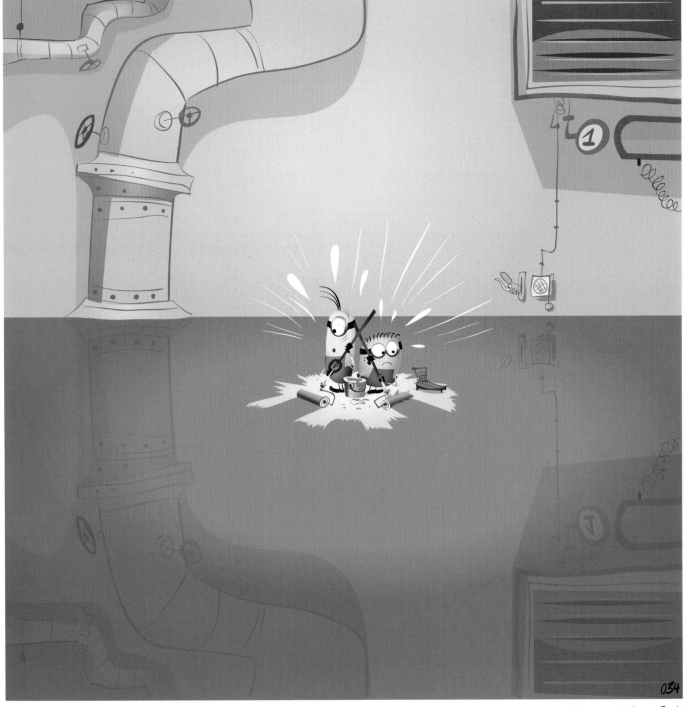

RENAUD + DiDiER 2014

RENAUD + DIDIER 2014

05

RENAUD + DIDIER 2014

RENAUD + DIDIER 2014

RENAUD + DIDIER 2014

RENAUD + DiDIER 2014

ORIGINAL!

The next day...

013

RENAUD + DIDIER 2014

RENAUD + DIDIER 2014

RENAUD + DIDIER 2014

RENAUD + DIDIER 2014

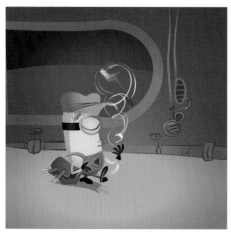

RENAUD + DIDIER 2014

REVAUD + DIDIER 2014

RENAUD + DIDIER 2014

RENAUD + DIDIER 2014

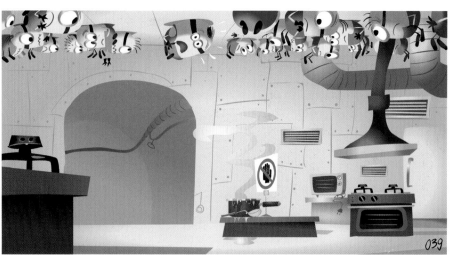

RENAUD + DIDIER 2014

023

RENAUD + DIDIER 2014

RENAUD + DIDIER 2014

020

RENAUD + DIDIER 2014

RENAUD + DIDIER 2014

The next day...

REVAUD + DIDIER 2014

RENAUD + DIDIER 2014

REVAUD + DIDIER 2014

RENAUD + DIDIER 2014

033

Renaud + Didier 2014

Find the Minion taking photos!